KIDS GRATITUDE JOURNAL

JOURNAL FOR KIDS TO PRACTICE GRATITUDE AND MINDFULNESS

This book belongs to:

_____

Copyright © 2020 Brenda Nathan
All rights reserved

No part of this publication may be reproduced,
distributed or transmitted in any form or by any
means, including photocopying, recording, or any
other electronic or mechanical methods, without
the prior written permission of the publisher.

ISBN: 978-1-952358-14-2

Limits of Liability and Disclaimer of Warranty

The author and publisher shall not be liable for
your misuse of this material. This book is strictly
for informational and educational purposes.

MY GRATITUDE DATE: _____ S M T W T F S

Today's message to myself...

Today I am grateful for...

Someone I could surprise with a note of appreciation or gift...

Something awesome that happened today...

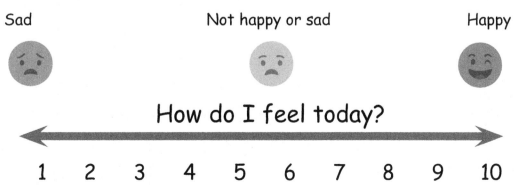

Sad   Not happy or sad   Happy

How do I feel today?

1 2 3 4 5 6 7 8 9 10

MY GRATITUDE DATE: _____ S M T W T F S

Today's message to myself...

Today I am grateful for...

Someone I could surprise with a note of appreciation or gift...

Something awesome that happened today...

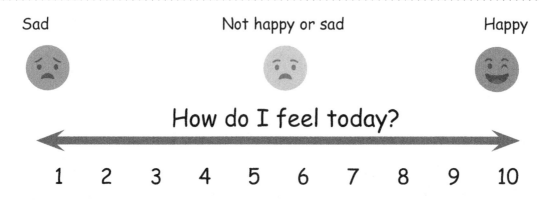

| Sad | Not happy or sad | Happy |

How do I feel today?

1　　2　　3　　4　　5　　6　　7　　8　　9　　10

MY GRATITUDE DATE: _____ S M T W T F S

Today's message to myself...

Today I am grateful for...

Someone I could surprise with a note of appreciation or gift...

Something awesome that happened today...

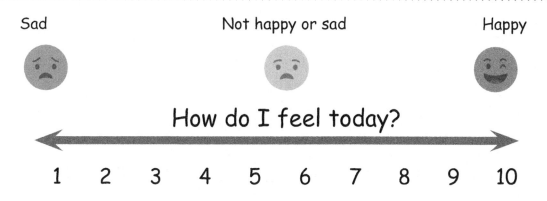

| Sad | Not happy or sad | Happy |

How do I feel today?

1   2   3   4   5   6   7   8   9   10

MY GRATITUDE DATE: _____ S M T W T F S

Today's message to myself...

Today I am grateful for...

Someone I could surprise with a note of appreciation or gift...

Something awesome that happened today...

| Sad | Not happy or sad | Happy |

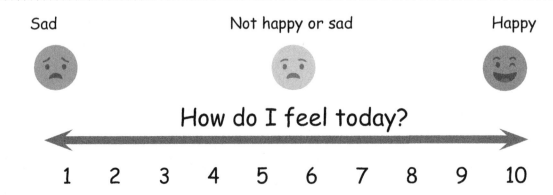

How do I feel today?

1 2 3 4 5 6 7 8 9 10

MY GRATITUDE DATE: _____ S M T W T F S

Today's message to myself...

Today I am grateful for...

Someone I could surprise with a note of appreciation or gift...

Something awesome that happened today...

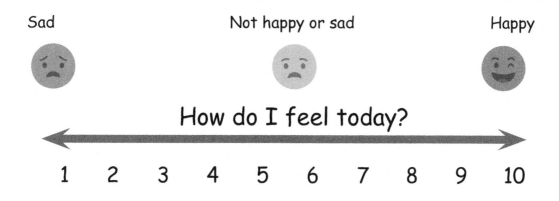

Sad   Not happy or sad   Happy

How do I feel today?

1   2   3   4   5   6   7   8   9   10

MY GRATITUDE DATE: _____ S M T W T F S

Today's message to myself...

Today I am grateful for...

Someone I could surprise with a note of appreciation or gift...

Something awesome that happened today...

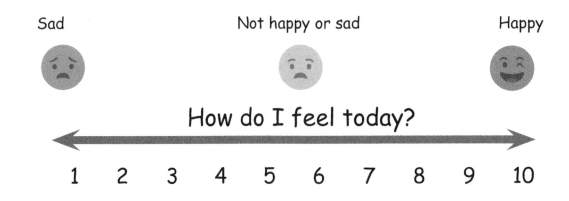

Sad   Not happy or sad   Happy

How do I feel today?

1   2   3   4   5   6   7   8   9   10

MY GRATITUDE DATE: _____ S M T W T F S

Today's message to myself...

Today I am grateful for...

Someone I could surprise with a note of appreciation or gift...

Something awesome that happened today...

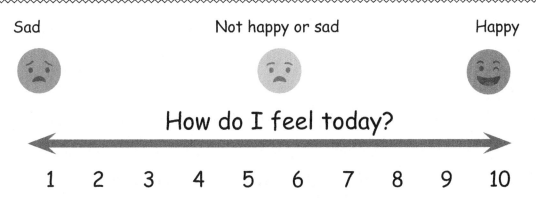

| Sad | Not happy or sad | Happy |

How do I feel today?

1   2   3   4   5   6   7   8   9   10

MY GRATITUDE DATE: _____ S M T W T F S

Today's message to myself...

Today I am grateful for...

Someone I could surprise with a note of appreciation or gift...

Something awesome that happened today...

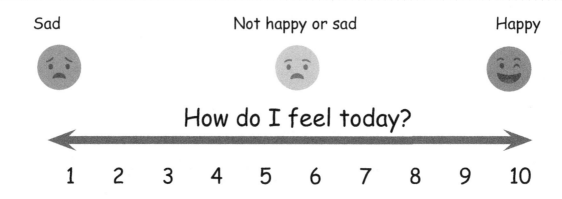

Sad   Not happy or sad   Happy

How do I feel today?

1   2   3   4   5   6   7   8   9   10

MY GRATITUDE DATE: _____ S M T W T F S

Today's message to myself...

Today I am grateful for...

Someone I could surprise with a note of appreciation or gift...

Something awesome that happened today...

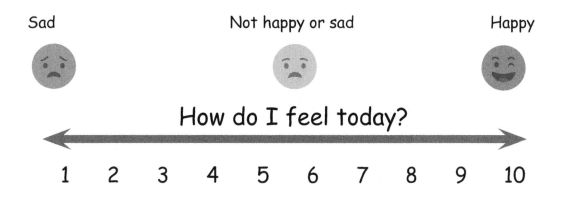

Sad   Not happy or sad   Happy

How do I feel today?

1   2   3   4   5   6   7   8   9   10

MY GRATITUDE DATE: _____ S M T W T F S

Today's message to myself...

Today I am grateful for...

Someone I could surprise with a note of appreciation or gift...

Something awesome that happened today...

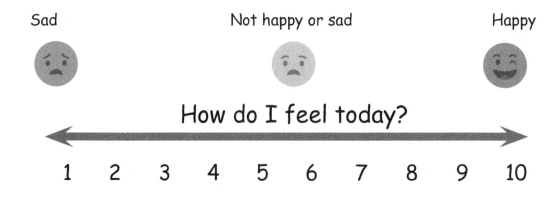

| Sad | Not happy or sad | Happy |

How do I feel today?

1   2   3   4   5   6   7   8   9   10

Draw Something

MY GRATITUDE DATE: _____ S M T W T F S

Today's message to myself...

Today I am grateful for...

Someone I could surprise with a note of appreciation or gift...

Thanks

Something awesome that happened today...

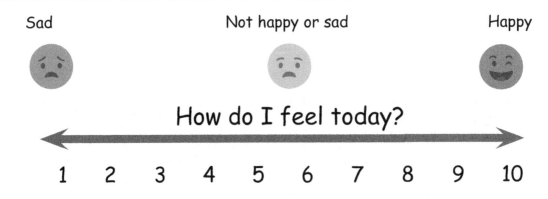

Sad	Not happy or sad	Happy

How do I feel today?

1   2   3   4   5   6   7   8   9   10

MY GRATITUDE DATE: _____ S M T W T F S

Today's message to myself...

Today I am grateful for...

Someone I could surprise with a note of appreciation or gift...

Something awesome that happened today...

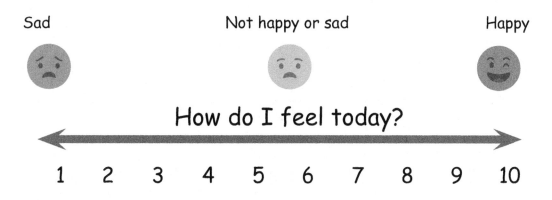

| Sad | Not happy or sad | Happy |

How do I feel today?

1   2   3   4   5   6   7   8   9   10

MY GRATITUDE DATE: _____ S M T W T F S

Today's message to myself...

Today I am grateful for...

Someone I could surprise with a note of appreciation or gift...

Something awesome that happened today...

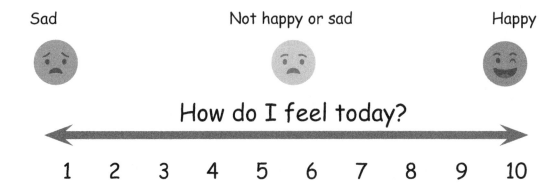

| Sad | Not happy or sad | Happy |

How do I feel today?

1   2   3   4   5   6   7   8   9   10

MY GRATITUDE DATE: _____ S M T W T F S

Today's message to myself...

Today I am grateful for...

Someone I could surprise with a note of appreciation or gift...

Something awesome that happened today...

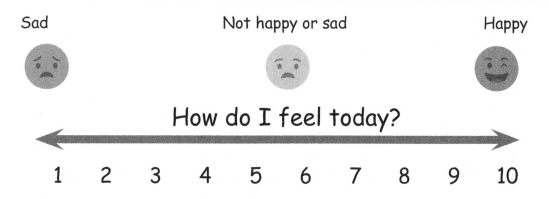

Sad   Not happy or sad   Happy

How do I feel today?

1   2   3   4   5   6   7   8   9   10

MY GRATITUDE DATE: _____ S M T W T F S

Today's message to myself...

Today I am grateful for...

Someone I could surprise with a note of appreciation or gift...

Thanks

Something awesome that happened today...

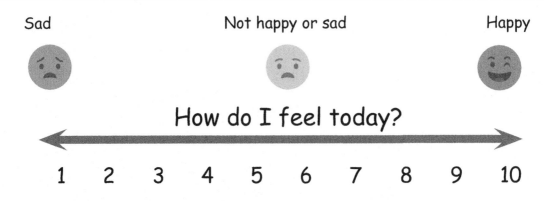

| Sad | Not happy or sad | Happy |

How do I feel today?

1   2   3   4   5   6   7   8   9   10

Today's message to myself...

Today I am grateful for...

Someone I could surprise with a note of appreciation or gift...

Something awesome that happened today...

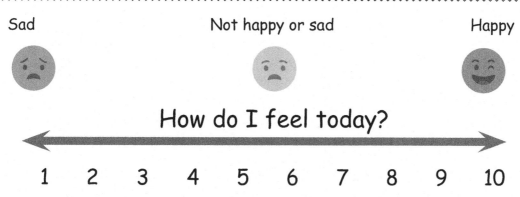

| Sad | Not happy or sad | Happy |

How do I feel today?

1   2   3   4   5   6   7   8   9   10

MY GRATITUDE DATE: _____ S M T W T F S

Today's message to myself...

Today I am grateful for...

Someone I could surprise with a note of appreciation or gift...

Something awesome that happened today...

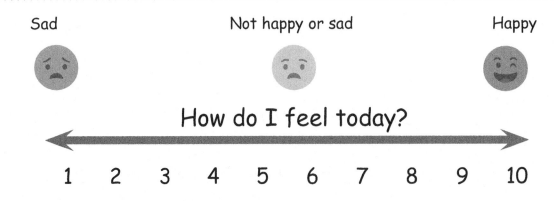

| Sad | Not happy or sad | Happy |

How do I feel today?

1   2   3   4   5   6   7   8   9   10

MY GRATITUDE DATE: _____ S M T W T F S

Today's message to myself...

Today I am grateful for...

Someone I could surprise with a note of appreciation or gift...

Something awesome that happened today...

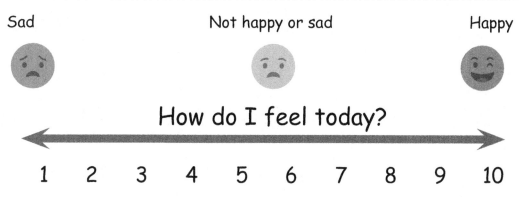

Sad   Not happy or sad   Happy

How do I feel today?

1   2   3   4   5   6   7   8   9   10

MY GRATITUDE DATE: _____ S M T W T F S

Today's message to myself...

Today I am grateful for...

Someone I could surprise with a note of appreciation or gift...

Something awesome that happened today...

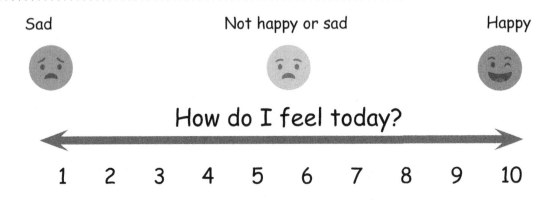

Sad	Not happy or sad	Happy

How do I feel today?

1 2 3 4 5 6 7 8 9 10

Draw Something

MY GRATITUDE DATE: _____ S M T W T F S

Today's message to myself...

Today I am grateful for...

Someone I could surprise with a note of appreciation or gift...

Something awesome that happened today...

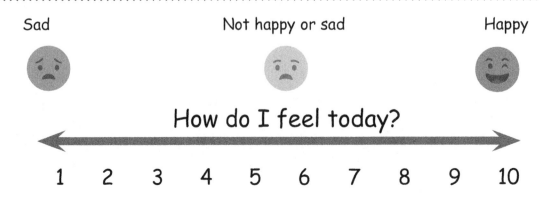

Sad	Not happy or sad	Happy

How do I feel today?

1   2   3   4   5   6   7   8   9   10

MY GRATITUDE DATE: _____ S M T W T F S

Today's message to myself...

Today I am grateful for...

Someone I could surprise with a note of appreciation or gift...

Something awesome that happened today...

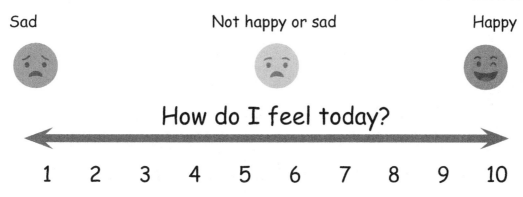

Sad	Not happy or sad	Happy

How do I feel today?

1 2 3 4 5 6 7 8 9 10

MY GRATITUDE DATE: _____ S M T W T F S

Today's message to myself...

Today I am grateful for...

Someone I could surprise with a note of appreciation or gift...

Something awesome that happened today...

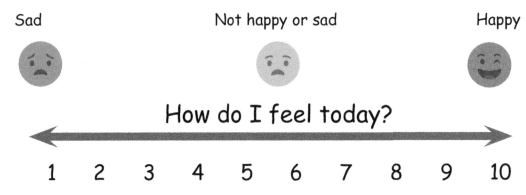

Sad   Not happy or sad   Happy

How do I feel today?

1 2 3 4 5 6 7 8 9 10

MY GRATITUDE DATE: _____ S M T W T F S

Today's message to myself...

Today I am grateful for...

Someone I could surprise with a note of appreciation or gift...

Something awesome that happened today...

Sad   Not happy or sad   Happy

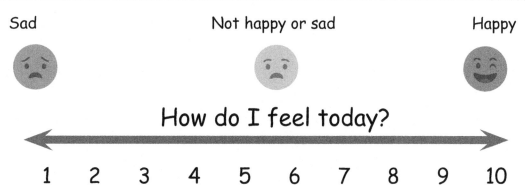

How do I feel today?

1   2   3   4   5   6   7   8   9   10

MY GRATITUDE DATE: _____ S M T W T F S

Today's message to myself...

Today I am grateful for...

Someone I could surprise with a note of appreciation or gift...

Something awesome that happened today...

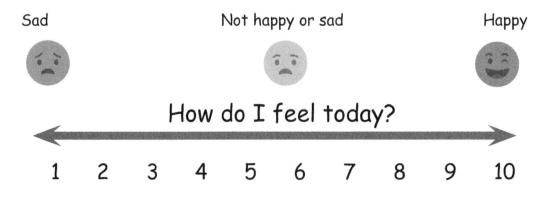

Sad   Not happy or sad   Happy

How do I feel today?

1 2 3 4 5 6 7 8 9 10

MY GRATITUDE DATE: _____ S M T W T F S

Today's message to myself...

Today I am grateful for...

Someone I could surprise with a note of appreciation or gift...

Something awesome that happened today...

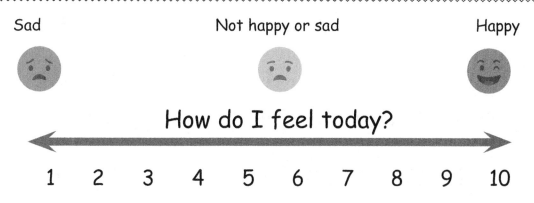

Sad   Not happy or sad   Happy

How do I feel today?

1   2   3   4   5   6   7   8   9   10

MY GRATITUDE DATE: _____ S M T W T F S

Today's message to myself...

Today I am grateful for...

Someone I could surprise with a note of appreciation or gift...

Something awesome that happened today...

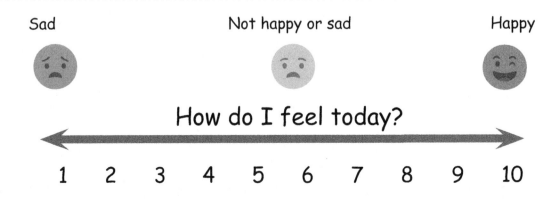

Sad	Not happy or sad	Happy

How do I feel today?

1 2 3 4 5 6 7 8 9 10

MY GRATITUDE DATE: _____ S M T W T F S

Today's message to myself...

Today I am grateful for...

Someone I could surprise with a note of appreciation or gift...

Something awesome that happened today...

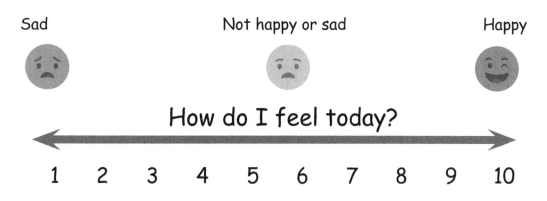

Sad   Not happy or sad   Happy

How do I feel today?

1   2   3   4   5   6   7   8   9   10

MY GRATITUDE DATE: _____ S M T W T F S

Today's message to myself...

Today I am grateful for...

Someone I could surprise with a note of appreciation or gift...

Something awesome that happened today...

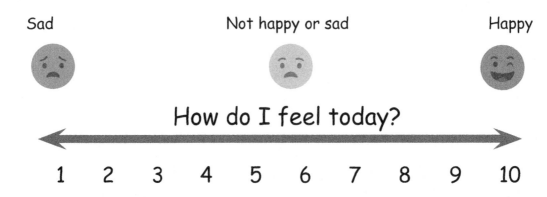

| Sad | Not happy or sad | Happy |

How do I feel today?

1   2   3   4   5   6   7   8   9   10

Draw Something

MY GRATITUDE DATE: _____ S M T W T F S

Today's message to myself...

Today I am grateful for...

Someone I could surprise with a note of appreciation or gift...

Something awesome that happened today...

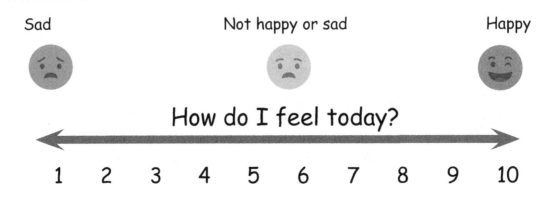

Sad   Not happy or sad   Happy

How do I feel today?

1   2   3   4   5   6   7   8   9   10

MY GRATITUDE DATE: _____ S M T W T F S

Today's message to myself...

Today I am grateful for...

Someone I could surprise with a note of appreciation or gift...

Something awesome that happened today...

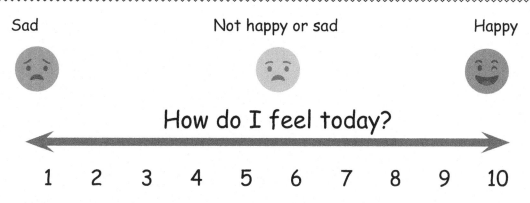

| Sad | Not happy or sad | Happy |

How do I feel today?

1   2   3   4   5   6   7   8   9   10

MY GRATITUDE DATE: _____ S M T W T F S

Today's message to myself...

Today I am grateful for...

Someone I could surprise with a note of appreciation or gift...

Something awesome that happened today...

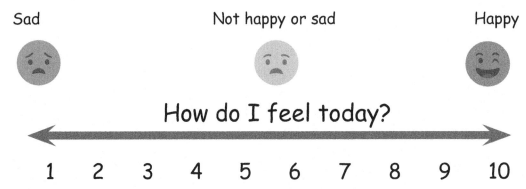

Sad   Not happy or sad   Happy

How do I feel today?

1   2   3   4   5   6   7   8   9   10

MY GRATITUDE DATE: _____ S M T W T F S

Today's message to myself...

Today I am grateful for...

Someone I could surprise with a note of appreciation or gift...

Thanks

Something awesome that happened today...

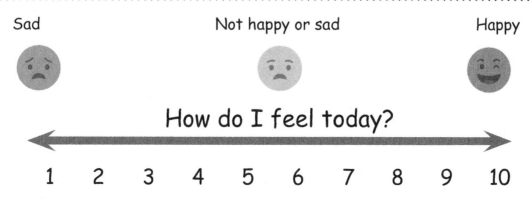

Sad | Not happy or sad | Happy

How do I feel today?

1   2   3   4   5   6   7   8   9   10

MY GRATITUDE DATE: _____ S M T W T F S

Today's message to myself...

Today I am grateful for...

Someone I could surprise with a note of appreciation or gift...

Something awesome that happened today...

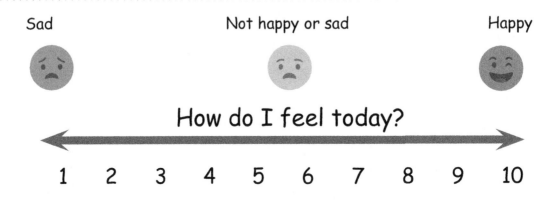

| Sad | Not happy or sad | Happy |

How do I feel today?

1 2 3 4 5 6 7 8 9 10

MY GRATITUDE DATE: _____ S M T W T F S

Today's message to myself...

Today I am grateful for...

Someone I could surprise with a note of appreciation or gift...

Something awesome that happened today...

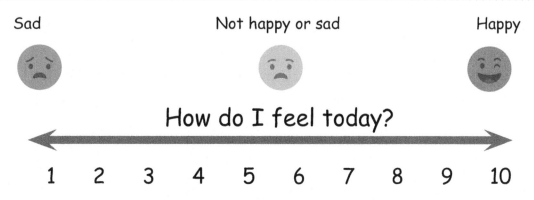

Sad   Not happy or sad   Happy

How do I feel today?

1   2   3   4   5   6   7   8   9   10

MY GRATITUDE DATE: _____ S M T W T F S

Today's message to myself...

Today I am grateful for...

Someone I could surprise with a note of appreciation or gift...

Something awesome that happened today...

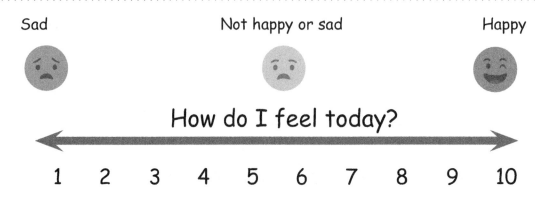

| Sad | Not happy or sad | Happy |

How do I feel today?

1 2 3 4 5 6 7 8 9 10

MY GRATITUDE DATE: _____ S M T W T F S

Today's message to myself...

Today I am grateful for...

Someone I could surprise with a note of appreciation or gift...

Something awesome that happened today...

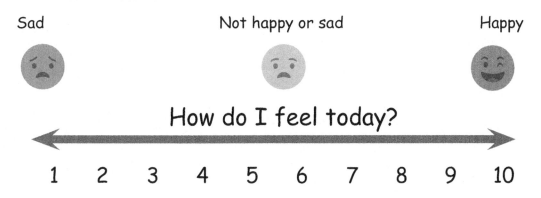

| Sad | Not happy or sad | Happy |

How do I feel today?

1   2   3   4   5   6   7   8   9   10

MY GRATITUDE DATE: _____ S M T W T F S

Today's message to myself...

Today I am grateful for...

Someone I could surprise with a note of appreciation or gift...

Something awesome that happened today...

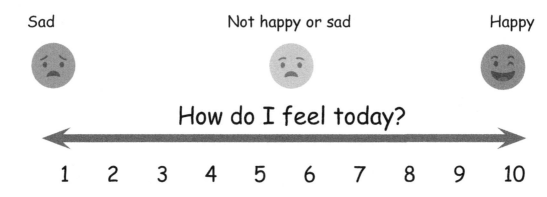

Sad   Not happy or sad   Happy

How do I feel today?

1 2 3 4 5 6 7 8 9 10

Draw Something

MY GRATITUDE DATE: _____ S M T W T F S

Today's message to myself...

Today I am grateful for...

Someone I could surprise with a note of appreciation or gift...

Something awesome that happened today...

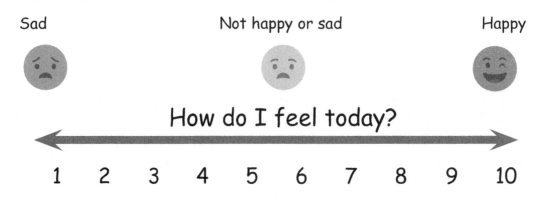

Sad   Not happy or sad   Happy

How do I feel today?

1   2   3   4   5   6   7   8   9   10

MY GRATITUDE DATE: _____ S M T W T F S

Today's message to myself…

Today I am grateful for…

Someone I could surprise with a note of appreciation or gift…

Something awesome that happened today…

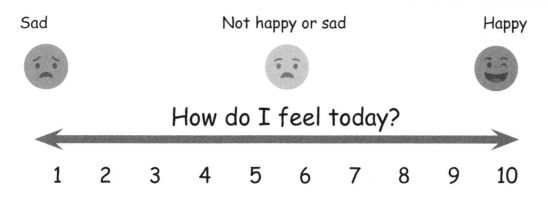

Sad   Not happy or sad   Happy

How do I feel today?

1   2   3   4   5   6   7   8   9   10

MY GRATITUDE DATE: _____ S M T W T F S

Today's message to myself...

Today I am grateful for...

Someone I could surprise with a note of appreciation or gift...

Something awesome that happened today...

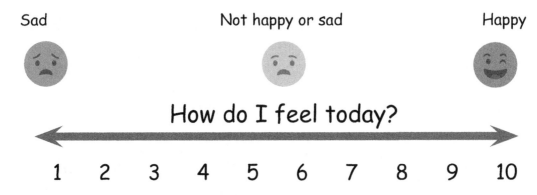

| Sad | Not happy or sad | Happy |

How do I feel today?

1 2 3 4 5 6 7 8 9 10

MY GRATITUDE DATE: _____ S M T W T F S

Today's message to myself...

Today I am grateful for...

Someone I could surprise with a note of appreciation or gift...

Something awesome that happened today...

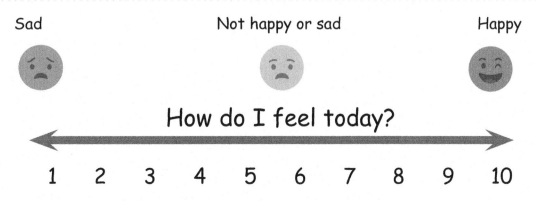

How do I feel today?

Sad   Not happy or sad   Happy

1   2   3   4   5   6   7   8   9   10

MY GRATITUDE DATE: _____ S M T W T F S

Today's message to myself...

Today I am grateful for...

Someone I could surprise with a note of appreciation or gift...

Something awesome that happened today...

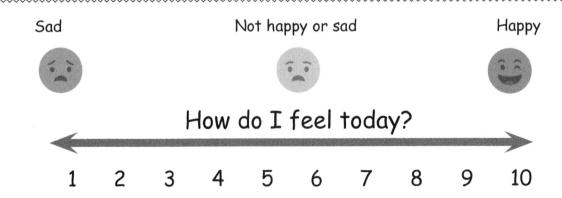

Sad	Not happy or sad	Happy

How do I feel today?

1   2   3   4   5   6   7   8   9   10

MY GRATITUDE DATE: _____ S M T W T F S

Today's message to myself...

Today I am grateful for...

Someone I could surprise with a note of appreciation or gift...

Something awesome that happened today...

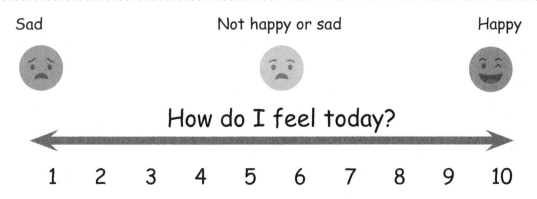

| Sad | Not happy or sad | Happy |

How do I feel today?

1   2   3   4   5   6   7   8   9   10

MY GRATITUDE DATE: _____ S M T W T F S

Today's message to myself...

Today I am grateful for...

Someone I could surprise with a note of appreciation or gift...

Something awesome that happened today...

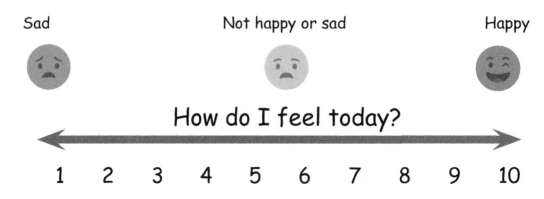

Sad	Not happy or sad	Happy

How do I feel today?

1   2   3   4   5   6   7   8   9   10

MY GRATITUDE DATE: _____ S M T W T F S

Today's message to myself...

Today I am grateful for...

Someone I could surprise with a note of appreciation or gift...

Something awesome that happened today...

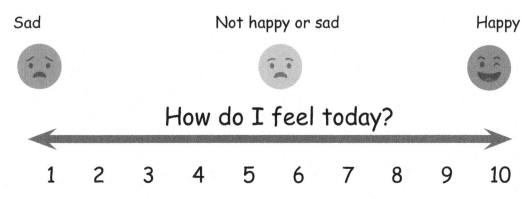

| Sad | Not happy or sad | Happy |

How do I feel today?

1   2   3   4   5   6   7   8   9   10

MY GRATITUDE DATE: _____ S M T W T F S

Today's message to myself...

Today I am grateful for...

Someone I could surprise with a note of appreciation or gift...

Something awesome that happened today...

Sad	Not happy or sad	Happy

How do I feel today?

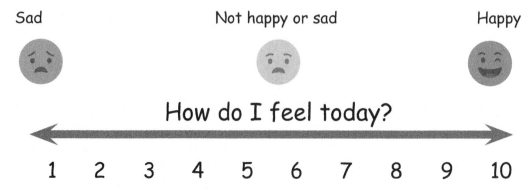

1   2   3   4   5   6   7   8   9   10

Draw Something

MY GRATITUDE DATE: _____ S M T W T F S

Today's message to myself...

Today I am grateful for...

Someone I could surprise with a note of appreciation or gift...

Something awesome that happened today...

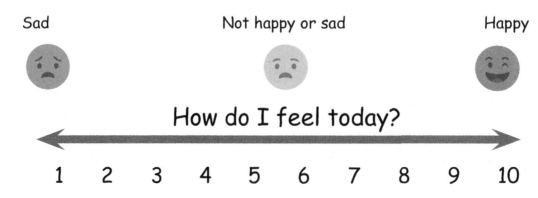

Sad | Not happy or sad | Happy

How do I feel today?

1 2 3 4 5 6 7 8 9 10

MY GRATITUDE DATE: _____ S M T W T F S

Today's message to myself...

Today I am grateful for...

Someone I could surprise with a note of appreciation or gift...

Something awesome that happened today...

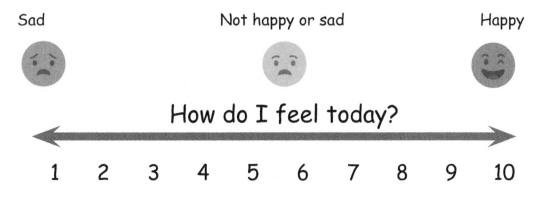

| Sad | Not happy or sad | Happy |

How do I feel today?

1   2   3   4   5   6   7   8   9   10

Today's message to myself...

Today I am grateful for...

Someone I could surprise with a note of appreciation or gift...

Something awesome that happened today...

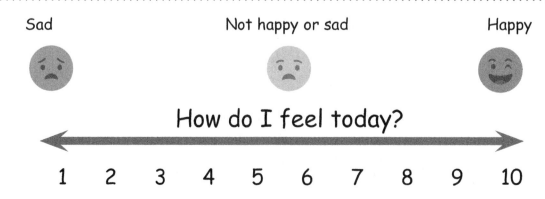

Sad	Not happy or sad	Happy

How do I feel today?

1 2 3 4 5 6 7 8 9 10

MY GRATITUDE DATE: _____ S M T W T F S

Today's message to myself...

Today I am grateful for...

Someone I could surprise with a note of appreciation or gift...

Something awesome that happened today...

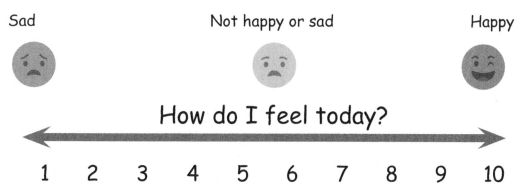

Sad   Not happy or sad   Happy

How do I feel today?

1   2   3   4   5   6   7   8   9   10

MY GRATITUDE DATE: _____ S M T W T F S

Today's message to myself...

Today I am grateful for...

Someone I could surprise with a note of appreciation or gift...

Something awesome that happened today...

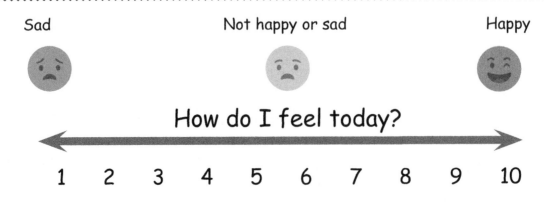

Sad	Not happy or sad	Happy

How do I feel today?

1   2   3   4   5   6   7   8   9   10

MY GRATITUDE DATE: _____ S M T W T F S

Today's message to myself...

Today I am grateful for...

Someone I could surprise with a note of appreciation or gift...

Something awesome that happened today...

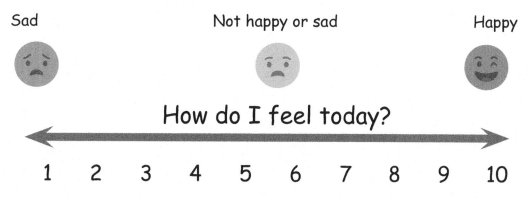

Sad   Not happy or sad   Happy

How do I feel today?

1   2   3   4   5   6   7   8   9   10

MY GRATITUDE DATE: _____ S M T W T F S

Today's message to myself...

Today I am grateful for...

Someone I could surprise with a note of appreciation or gift...

Something awesome that happened today...

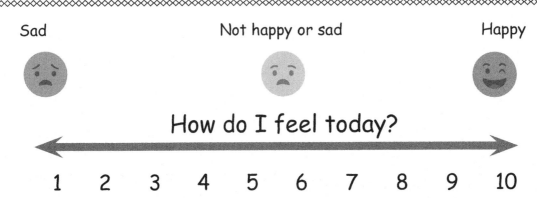

Sad	Not happy or sad	Happy

How do I feel today?

1　2　3　4　5　6　7　8　9　10

MY GRATITUDE DATE: _____ S M T W T F S

Today's message to myself...

Today I am grateful for...

Someone I could surprise with a note of appreciation or gift...

Something awesome that happened today...

| Sad | Not happy or sad | Happy |

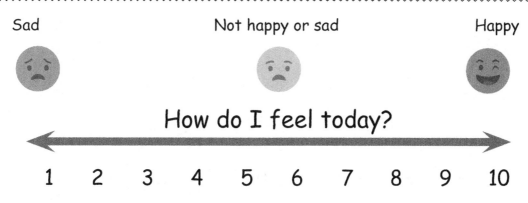

How do I feel today?

1   2   3   4   5   6   7   8   9   10

MY GRATITUDE DATE: _____ S M T W T F S

Today's message to myself...

Today I am grateful for...

Someone I could surprise with a note of appreciation or gift...

Thanks

Something awesome that happened today...

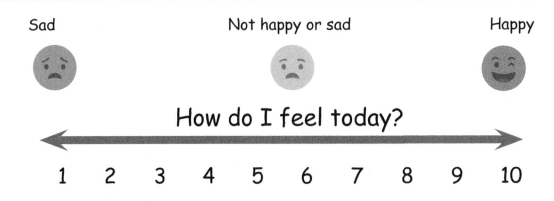

Sad	Not happy or sad	Happy

How do I feel today?

1 2 3 4 5 6 7 8 9 10

Draw Something

MY GRATITUDE DATE: _____ S M T W T F S

Today's message to myself...

Today I am grateful for...

Someone I could surprise with a note of appreciation or gift...

Something awesome that happened today...

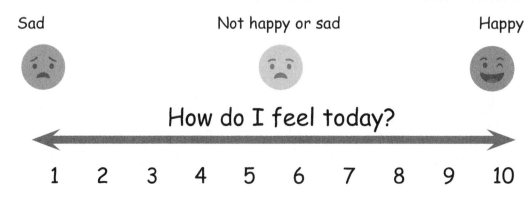

| Sad | Not happy or sad | Happy |

How do I feel today?

1 2 3 4 5 6 7 8 9 10

MY GRATITUDE DATE: _____ S M T W T F S

Today's message to myself...

Today I am grateful for...

Someone I could surprise with a note of appreciation or gift...

Something awesome that happened today...

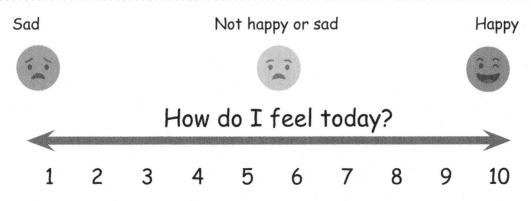

Sad   Not happy or sad   Happy

How do I feel today?

1   2   3   4   5   6   7   8   9   10

MY GRATITUDE DATE: _____ S M T W T F S

Today's message to myself...

Today I am grateful for...

Someone I could surprise with a note of appreciation or gift...

Something awesome that happened today...

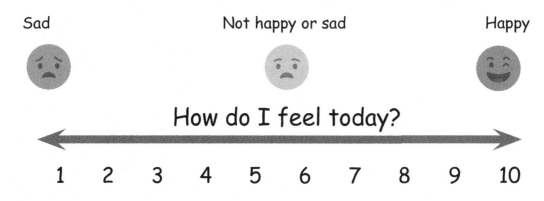

| Sad | Not happy or sad | Happy |

How do I feel today?

1   2   3   4   5   6   7   8   9   10

MY GRATITUDE DATE: _____ S M T W T F S

Today's message to myself...

Today I am grateful for...

Someone I could surprise with a note of appreciation or gift...

Something awesome that happened today...

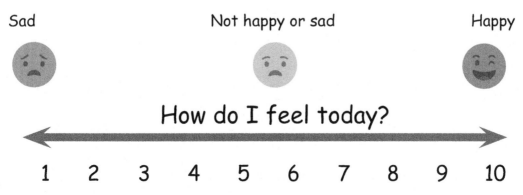

Sad   Not happy or sad   Happy

How do I feel today?

1   2   3   4   5   6   7   8   9   10

MY GRATITUDE DATE: _____ S M T W T F S

Today's message to myself...

Today I am grateful for...

Someone I could surprise with a note of appreciation or gift...

Something awesome that happened today...

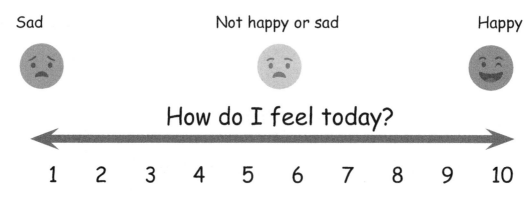

| Sad | Not happy or sad | Happy |

How do I feel today?

1 2 3 4 5 6 7 8 9 10

MY GRATITUDE DATE: _____ S M T W T F S

Today's message to myself...

Today I am grateful for...

Someone I could surprise with a note of appreciation or gift...

Something awesome that happened today...

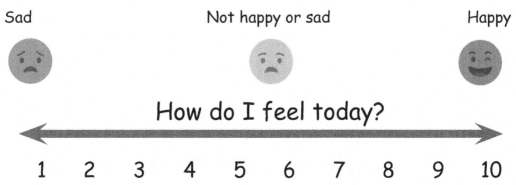

Sad   Not happy or sad   Happy

How do I feel today?

1 2 3 4 5 6 7 8 9 10

MY GRATITUDE DATE: _____ S M T W T F S

Today's message to myself...

Today I am grateful for...

Someone I could surprise with a note of appreciation or gift...

Something awesome that happened today...

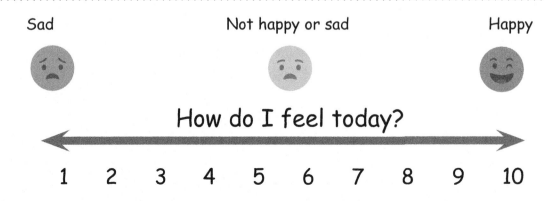

Sad   Not happy or sad   Happy

How do I feel today?

1   2   3   4   5   6   7   8   9   10

MY GRATITUDE DATE: _____ S M T W T F S

Today's message to myself...

Today I am grateful for...

Someone I could surprise with a note of appreciation or gift...

Something awesome that happened today...

Sad   Not happy or sad   Happy

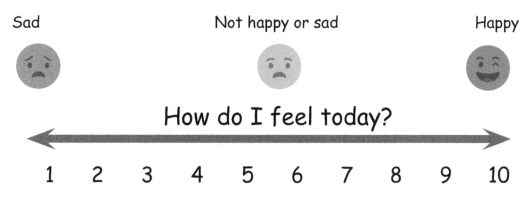

How do I feel today?

1   2   3   4   5   6   7   8   9   10

MY GRATITUDE DATE: _____ S M T W T F S

Today's message to myself...

Today I am grateful for...

Someone I could surprise with a note of appreciation or gift...

Something awesome that happened today...

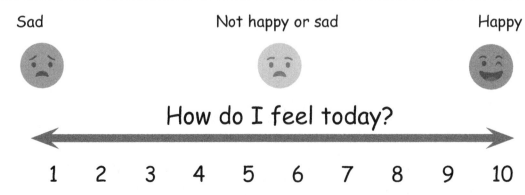

| Sad | Not happy or sad | Happy |

How do I feel today?

1   2   3   4   5   6   7   8   9   10

Draw Something

MY GRATITUDE DATE: _____ S M T W T F S

Today's message to myself...

Today I am grateful for...

Someone I could surprise with a note of appreciation or gift...

Something awesome that happened today...

| Sad | Not happy or sad | Happy |

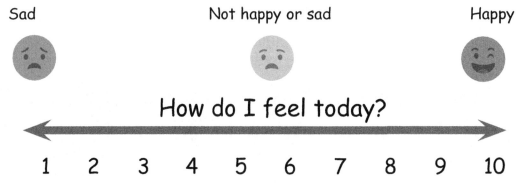

How do I feel today?

1 2 3 4 5 6 7 8 9 10

MY GRATITUDE DATE: _____ S M T W T F S

Today's message to myself...

Today I am grateful for...

Someone I could surprise with a note of appreciation or gift...

Something awesome that happened today...

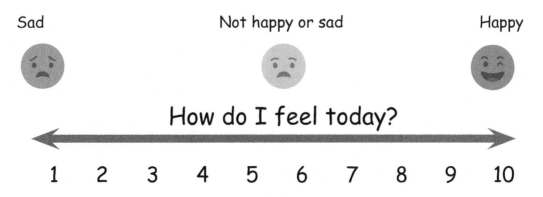

| Sad | Not happy or sad | Happy |

How do I feel today?

1 2 3 4 5 6 7 8 9 10

MY GRATITUDE DATE: _____ S M T W T F S

Today's message to myself...

Today I am grateful for...

Someone I could surprise with a note of appreciation or gift...

Something awesome that happened today...

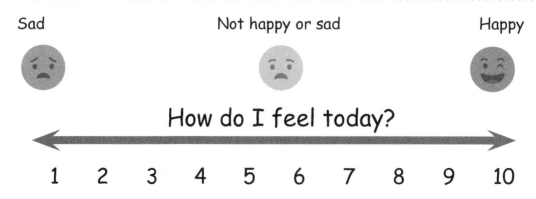

Sad　　　　　Not happy or sad　　　　　Happy

How do I feel today?

1　2　3　4　5　6　7　8　9　10

MY GRATITUDE DATE: _____ S M T W T F S

Today's message to myself...

Today I am grateful for...

Someone I could surprise with a note of appreciation or gift...

Something awesome that happened today...

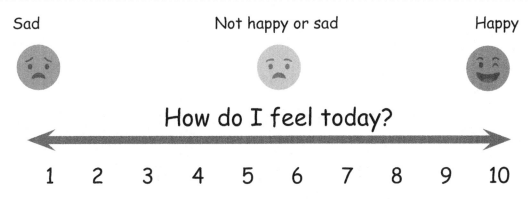

| Sad | Not happy or sad | Happy |

How do I feel today?

1   2   3   4   5   6   7   8   9   10

MY GRATITUDE DATE: _____ S M T W T F S

Today's message to myself...

Today I am grateful for...

Someone I could surprise with a note of appreciation or gift...

Something awesome that happened today...

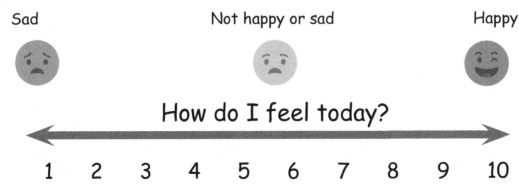

Sad   Not happy or sad   Happy

How do I feel today?

1   2   3   4   5   6   7   8   9   10

MY GRATITUDE DATE: _____ S M T W T F S

Today's message to myself...

Today I am grateful for...

Someone I could surprise with a note of appreciation or gift...

Something awesome that happened today...

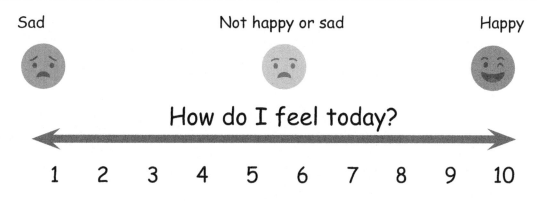

| Sad | Not happy or sad | Happy |

How do I feel today?

1   2   3   4   5   6   7   8   9   10

MY GRATITUDE DATE: _____ S M T W T F S

Today's message to myself...

Today I am grateful for...

Someone I could surprise with a note of appreciation or gift...

Something awesome that happened today...

Sad	Not happy or sad	Happy

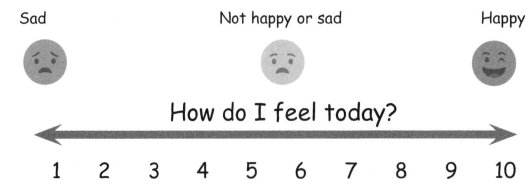

How do I feel today?

1   2   3   4   5   6   7   8   9   10

MY GRATITUDE DATE: _____ S M T W T F S

Today's message to myself...

Today I am grateful for...

Someone I could surprise with a note of appreciation or gift...

Something awesome that happened today...

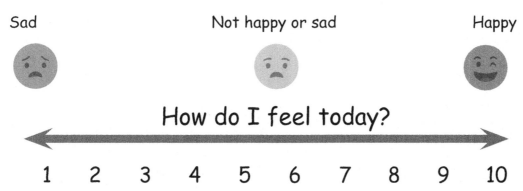

Sad   Not happy or sad   Happy

How do I feel today?

1 2 3 4 5 6 7 8 9 10

MY GRATITUDE DATE: _____ S M T W T F S

Today's message to myself...

Today I am grateful for...

Someone I could surprise with a note of appreciation or gift...

Something awesome that happened today...

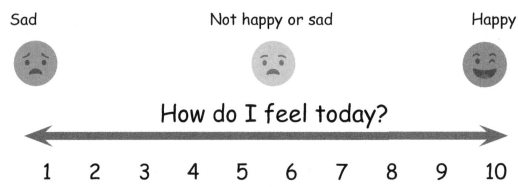

| Sad | Not happy or sad | Happy |

How do I feel today?

1   2   3   4   5   6   7   8   9   10

Draw Something

MY GRATITUDE DATE: _____ S M T W T F S

Today's message to myself...

Today I am grateful for...

Someone I could surprise with a note of appreciation or gift...

Something awesome that happened today...

Sad   Not happy or sad   Happy

How do I feel today?

1   2   3   4   5   6   7   8   9   10

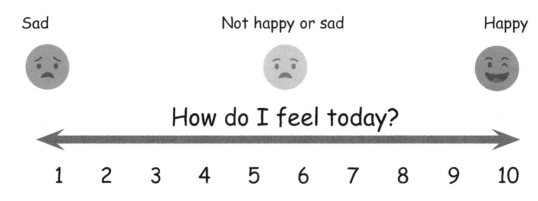

MY GRATITUDE DATE: _____ S M T W T F S

Today's message to myself...

Today I am grateful for...

Someone I could surprise with a note of appreciation or gift...

Something awesome that happened today...

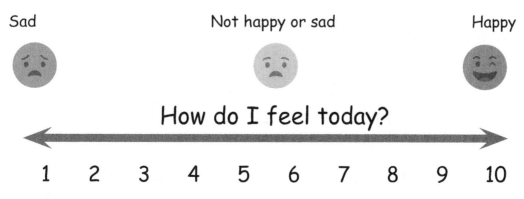

Sad   Not happy or sad   Happy

How do I feel today?

1   2   3   4   5   6   7   8   9   10

MY GRATITUDE DATE: _____ S M T W F S

Today's message to myself...

Today I am grateful for...

Someone I could surprise with a note of appreciation or gift...

Something awesome that happened today...

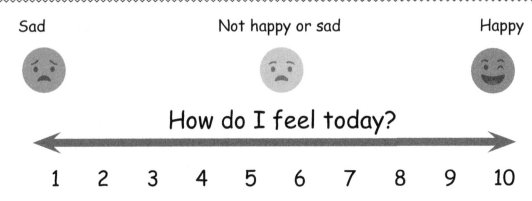

| Sad | Not happy or sad | Happy |

How do I feel today?

1   2   3   4   5   6   7   8   9   10

MY GRATITUDE DATE: _____ S M T W T F S

Today's message to myself...

Today I am grateful for...

Someone I could surprise with a note of appreciation or gift...

Something awesome that happened today...

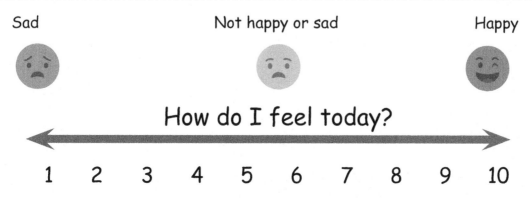

Sad	Not happy or sad	Happy

How do I feel today?

1   2   3   4   5   6   7   8   9   10

MY GRATITUDE DATE: _____ S M T W T F S

Today's message to myself...

Today I am grateful for...

Someone I could surprise with a note of appreciation or gift...

Something awesome that happened today...

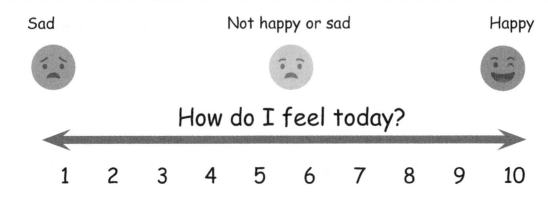

MY GRATITUDE DATE: _____ S M T W T F S

Today's message to myself...

Today I am grateful for...

Someone I could surprise with a note of appreciation or gift...

Something awesome that happened today...

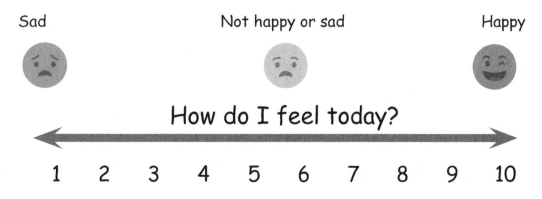

| Sad | Not happy or sad | Happy |

How do I feel today?

1   2   3   4   5   6   7   8   9   10

MY GRATITUDE DATE: _____ S M T W T F S

Today's message to myself...

Today I am grateful for...

Someone I could surprise with a note of appreciation or gift...

Something awesome that happened today...

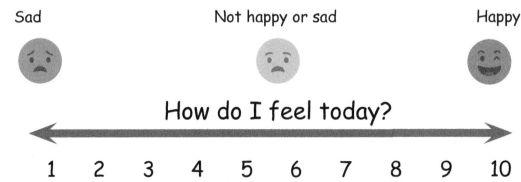

Sad   Not happy or sad   Happy

How do I feel today?

1   2   3   4   5   6   7   8   9   10

MY GRATITUDE DATE: _____ S M T W T F S

Today's Message to Myself...

Today I am grateful for...

Someone I could surprise with a note of appreciation or gift...

Something awesome that happened today...

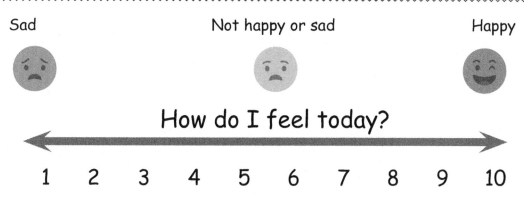

Sad   Not happy or sad   Happy

How do I feel today?

1 2 3 4 5 6 7 8 9 10

MY GRATITUDE DATE: _____ S M T W T F S

Today's message to myself...

Today I am grateful for...

Someone I could surprise with a note of appreciation or gift...

Something awesome that happened today...

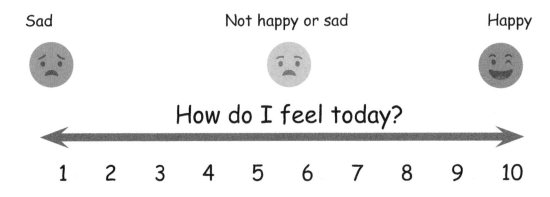

Sad   Not happy or sad   Happy

How do I feel today?

1   2   3   4   5   6   7   8   9   10

Draw Something

MY GRATITUDE DATE: _____ S M T W T F S

Today's message to myself...

Today I am grateful for...

Someone I could surprise with a note of appreciation or gift...

Something awesome that happened today...

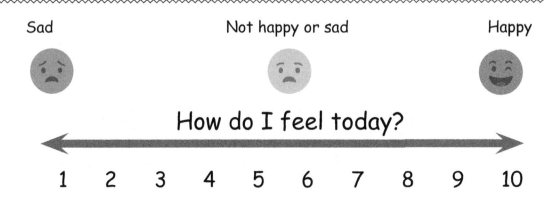

Sad   Not happy or sad   Happy

How do I feel today?

1 2 3 4 5 6 7 8 9 10

MY GRATITUDE DATE: _____ S M T W T F S

Today's message to myself...

Today I am grateful for...

Someone I could surprise with a note of appreciation or gift...

Something awesome that happened today...

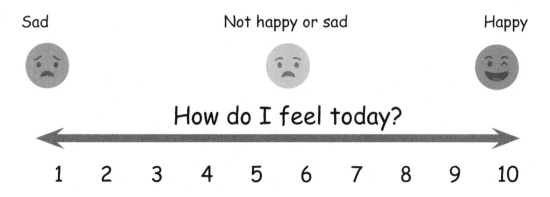

| Sad | Not happy or sad | Happy |

How do I feel today?

1   2   3   4   5   6   7   8   9   10

MY GRATITUDE DATE: _____ S M T W T F S

Today's message to myself...

Today I am grateful for...

Someone I could surprise with a note of appreciation or gift...

Something awesome that happened today...

Sad	Not happy or sad	Happy

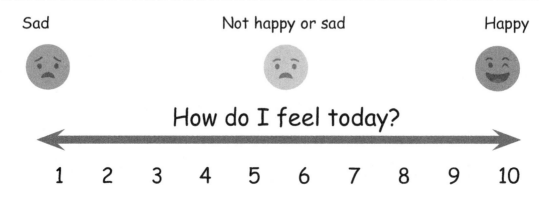

How do I feel today?

1   2   3   4   5   6   7   8   9   10

MY GRATITUDE DATE: _____ S M T W T F S

Today's message to myself...

Today I am grateful for...

Someone I could surprise with a note of appreciation or gift...

Something awesome that happened today...

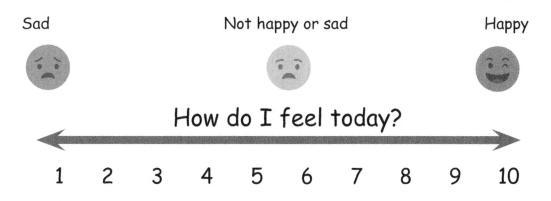

Sad   Not happy or sad   Happy

How do I feel today?

1   2   3   4   5   6   7   8   9   10

MY GRATITUDE DATE: _____ S M T W T F S

Today's message to myself...

Today I am grateful for...

Someone I could surprise with a note of appreciation or gift...

Something awesome that happened today...

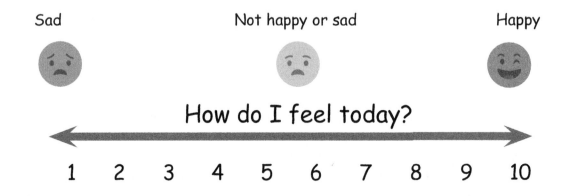

| Sad | Not happy or sad | Happy |

How do I feel today?

1   2   3   4   5   6   7   8   9   10

MY GRATITUDE DATE: _____ S M T W T F S

Today's message to myself...

Today I am grateful for...

Someone I could surprise with a note of appreciation or gift...

Something awesome that happened today...

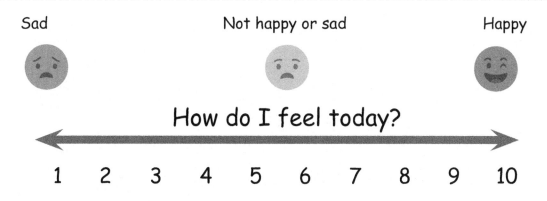

Sad	Not happy or sad	Happy

How do I feel today?

1   2   3   4   5   6   7   8   9   10

MY GRATITUDE DATE: _____ S M T W T F S

Today's message to myself...

Today I am grateful for...

Someone I could surprise with a note of appreciation or gift...

Something awesome that happened today...

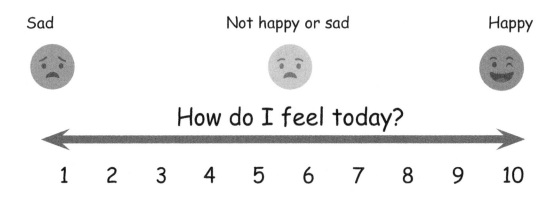

Sad   Not happy or sad   Happy

How do I feel today?

1   2   3   4   5   6   7   8   9   10

MY GRATITUDE DATE: _____ S M T W T F S

Today's message to myself...

Today I am grateful for...

Someone I could surprise with a note of appreciation or gift...

Something awesome that happened today...

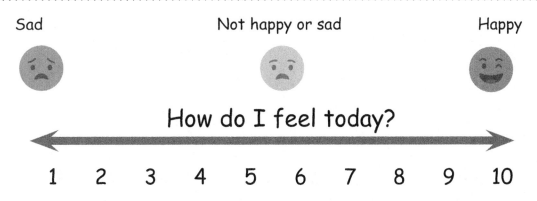

| Sad | Not happy or sad | Happy |

How do I feel today?

1   2   3   4   5   6   7   8   9   10

MY GRATITUDE DATE: _____ S M T W T F S

Today's message to myself...

Today I am grateful for...

Someone I could surprise with a note of appreciation or gift...

Something awesome that happened today...

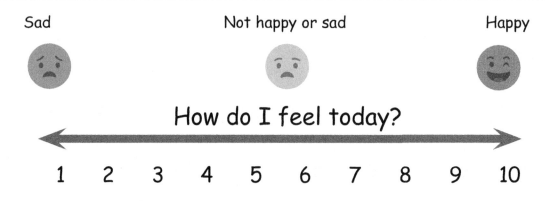

| Sad | Not happy or sad | Happy |

How do I feel today?

1 2 3 4 5 6 7 8 9 10

Draw Something

MY GRATITUDE DATE: _____ S M T W T F S

Today's message to myself...

Today I am grateful for...

Someone I could surprise with a note of appreciation or gift...

Something awesome that happened today...

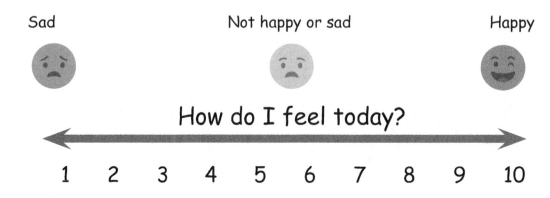

| Sad | Not happy or sad | Happy |

How do I feel today?

1   2   3   4   5   6   7   8   9   10

MY GRATITUDE DATE: _____ S M T W T F S

Today's message to myself...

Today I am grateful for...

Someone I could surprise with a note of appreciation or gift...

Something awesome that happened today...

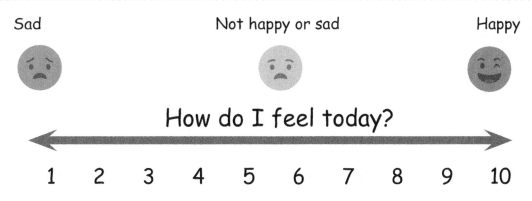

Sad   Not happy or sad   Happy

How do I feel today?

1   2   3   4   5   6   7   8   9   10

MY GRATITUDE DATE: _____ S M T W T F S

Today's message to myself...

Today I am grateful for...

Someone I could surprise with a note of appreciation or gift...

Something awesome that happened today...

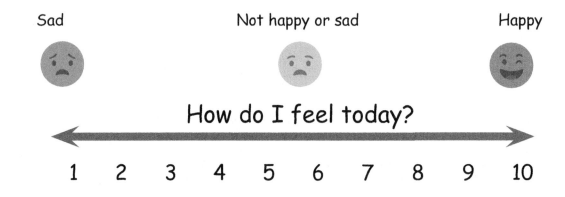

Sad	Not happy or sad	Happy

How do I feel today?

1 2 3 4 5 6 7 8 9 10

MY GRATITUDE DATE: _____ S M T W T F S

Today's message to myself...

Today I am grateful for...

Someone I could surprise with a note of appreciation or gift...

Something awesome that happened today...

Sad	Not happy or sad	Happy

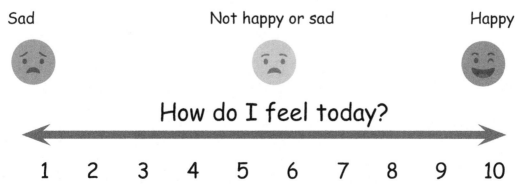

How do I feel today?

1   2   3   4   5   6   7   8   9   10

MY GRATITUDE DATE: _____ S M T W T F S

Today's message to myself...

Today I am grateful for...

Someone I could surprise with a note of appreciation or gift...

Something awesome that happened today...

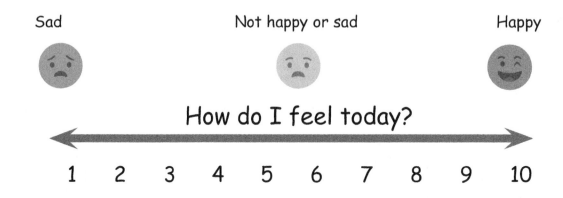

Sad   Not happy or sad   Happy

How do I feel today?

1   2   3   4   5   6   7   8   9   10

MY GRATITUDE DATE: _____ S M T W T F S

Today's Message to Myself...

Today I am grateful for...

Someone I could surprise with a note of appreciation or gift...

Something awesome that happened today...

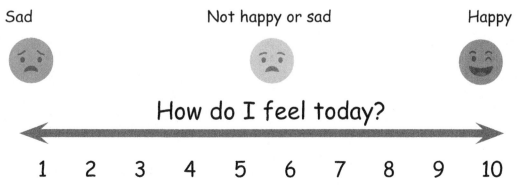

Sad   Not happy or sad   Happy

How do I feel today?

1   2   3   4   5   6   7   8   9   10

MY GRATITUDE DATE: _____ S M T W T F S

Today's message to myself...

Today I am grateful for...

Someone I could surprise with a note of appreciation or gift...

Something awesome that happened today...

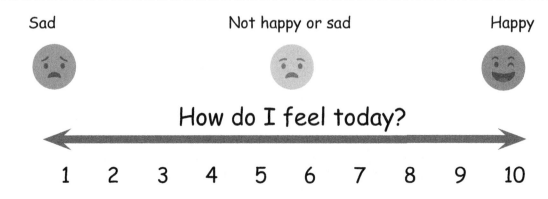

Sad   Not happy or sad   Happy

How do I feel today?

1   2   3   4   5   6   7   8   9   10

MY GRATITUDE DATE: _____ S M T W T F S

Today's message to myself...

Today I am grateful for...

Someone I could surprise with a note of appreciation or gift...

Something awesome that happened today...

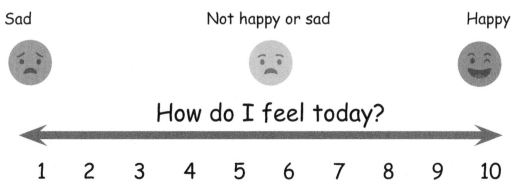

| Sad | Not happy or sad | Happy |

How do I feel today?

1   2   3   4   5   6   7   8   9   10

MY GRATITUDE DATE: _____ S M T W T F S

Today's message to myself...

Today I am grateful for...

Someone I could surprise with a note of appreciation or gift...

Something awesome that happened today...

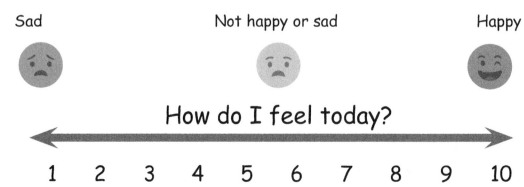

Sad	Not happy or sad	Happy

How do I feel today?

1   2   3   4   5   6   7   8   9   10

Made in the USA
Coppell, TX
10 December 2020

44033908R00063